DALEK SURVIVAL GUIDE

Published by BBC Worldwide Ltd,
80 Wood Lane, London W12 0TT

First published 2002
Text copyright © BBC Worldwide Ltd

ISBN 0 563 48600 7

Commissioning Editor: Ben Dunn
Project Editors: April Warman and Rebecca Kincaid
Designer: Martin Hendry
Illustrator: Alan Burton
Cover illustration: Emma Judd
Production Controller: Kenneth McKay
Contributors: Justin Richards, Nicholas Briggs, Stephen Cole,
Jacqueline Rayner and Mike Tucker

Set in Adobe Caslon and Univers
Printed and bound in Great Britain by the Bath Press
Cover printed by Belmont Press, Northampton

Dedicated to the memory
of Terry Nation

CONTENTS

GENERAL
INFORMATION

This *Dalek Survival Guide* has been put together to give you the most comprehensive guide to the Daleks assembled since Terry Nation first discovered and translated the *Dalek Chronicles* and alerted this world and others to their threat. With this book, we are sounding a wake-up call to the menace the Daleks pose, and hoping to equip you, to some extent, to deal with this terrifying threat. The Daleks are out there, the Daleks are coming, and people in bungalows and ground-floor flats should be especially wary.

The information gathered here comes from a variety of sources, and is based on research notes, scientific reports and various recently disclosed classified papers. But we were also fortunate enough to discover a large amount of material from the future, delivered to us in a battered Gladstone bag. Strangely, when the bag was emptied more papers and documents came out of it than could possibly have fitted inside.

With this wealth of evidence now available, we have decided that it is time to go public and reveal the true extent of the Dalek menace. Now everyone on our planet can learn everything there is to know about the Daleks. We shall be prepared for the Daleks − in the present, the past and the future.

HOW THIS GUIDE IS ORGANIZED

For ease of reference, this guide is split into three sections:

1 **Know Your Enemy** – this section provides general background information about the Daleks and how to react to a Dalek invasion or incursion.

2 **Supplementary Data** – this section provides detailed information on all aspects of the Dalek race.

3 **FAQs** – this section answers frequently asked questions that may not be covered elsewhere.

THE DALEKS – A BRIEF DESCRIPTION AND OVERVIEW

It is perhaps surprising that there are still people in the world today who have not heard of the Daleks, people who do not realize their terrible threat. For these few, this section gives a brief overview of the Daleks.

Originally from the planet Skaro, the Daleks are an intelligent alien life-form. According to the most plausible of the theories about the history and evolution of the Daleks, the genetic form of the Dalek creature was created by the scientist Davros. Believing that it was the fate of his race, the Kaleds, to mutate as a result of their thousand-year war against the Thals, he experimented to discover the ultimate form of that mutation. This he then genetically engineered to 'improve' its make-up – removing emotions such as pity and remorse and instilling heightened aggression towards all other forms of life. He placed the final creature inside specially designed travel machines. It is the form and shape of this tank-like travel machine that is so well recognized by humans today. The Dalek.

The true form of the creature inside the travel machine is open to debate, but it is known to be horribly mutated as a result of the neutronic war with the Thals.

According to Edward Waterfield's 1866 monograph *On Daleks*, the Dalek machines are powered by static electricity and operated by the Dalek inside using psycho-kinesis. The machine is equipped with an eye on a stalk on the top, domed section. It also has an arm with a sucker attachment that can be extended to an impressive length (though this may be exchanged for other appendages depending on the situation), and a fearsome gun that fires ruby rays. This weapon can be used to stun or more usually to kill.

The Daleks have only one ambition, one driving force – to conquer all life of any sort wherever they find it. There is much debate about why they do this, but the most plausible explanation seems to be that they have a violent dislike for anything that is unlike themselves – any form of life that still has an independently functioning body. These they hunt down and exterminate. Subjugate and conquer. Destroy and rule...

TERRY NATION – DALEK CHRONICLER

Based on the *Dalek Chronicles* discovered and translated by Terry Nation.

These words have appeared at the front of several previous Dalek reference books. But just who was Terry Nation? And what were the *Dalek Chronicles*?

Terry Nation was born in Wales in 1930, and died at the age of 66 in the USA. The work for which he will be best-remembered remains his discovery of the *Dalek Chronicles* and his contributions to the BBC documentary series *Doctor Who*, which was devised to alert the general public to the various alien dangers we face, while at the same time serving as a dramatized biography of the central character, the Doctor (see The Doctor – Man or Myth? on page 19).

Typically, Nation was modest about his achievement.

In his seminal introduction to one of the reference works that sought to document the threat of the Daleks in a serious and coherent manner, Nation said, 'The information in this book is based on the *Dalek Chronicles*, which I discovered and translated.'

This simple statement does little to suggest the extraordinary lengths to which Nation went in persuading the BBC to include material adapted from these chronicles in what was considered at the time to be a children's science-fiction programme with mildly educational overtones. Nation saw – as we have realized since – that this was exactly the place to start seeding the information that he hoped would one day help to preserve the safety of the human race itself.

His subsequent contributions to the series, which is now seen as a masterful biography of one of the most extraordinary and significant characters in history, continued for the most part to document the threat of the Daleks. Nation's quest to understand and communicate the contents of the holographic datacubes that formed the *Dalek Chronicles* never ceased.

Most of the documentary evidence provided by the BBC was scripted by Nation himself, but even when he was busy on other projects he was still able to provide research materials and insight so that other writers could contribute their own interpretations of events detailed in the *Dalek Chronicles*.

THE DOCTOR – MAN OR MYTH?

The Doctor has been described as 'a Complex Space-Time Event.' This description helps us about as much as any other in defining who – or rather what – the being known as the Doctor actually is.

It is usually assumed that the Doctor is a myth, a figure conjured from fiction to explain and excuse all sorts of events in our history and throughout the history of the whole universe. He is rumoured to have two hearts and to be able to change his appearance when others would die of their injuries. This is of course very unlikely, though not as unlikely as the suggestion that he travels through time and space in an outdated Police Telephone Box.

Incredible as all this may seem, there is a wealth of evidence to suggest that the Doctor really does exist and is not, as has been suggested, a codename that covers several different UNIT agents.

Whoever he is, the Doctor is inextricably linked with the United Nations Intelligence Taskforce. He is employed on occasion as their Scientific Adviser, though his 'name' does not appear in any official documentation.

Of course, the most detailed, informative and in many ways insidious information about the Doctor is provided by the BBC's series of dramatized biographies transmitted as family entertainment between 1963 and 1996. This has been followed by various published biographies presented in mock-fictional form as segments of the Doctor's lives. While some of these are of dubious provenance, two things emerge as incontrovertibly true:

1 **The Doctor exists.**

2 **The Doctor knows more about the Daleks than any other person, living or exterminated.**

But whatever his background and history, we owe the Doctor a huge debt of gratitude. He has fought the Daleks throughout all of time and space. There are also suggestions that it was the Doctor who collected and collated much of the material on Daleks that we now possess. Once again, the Doctor has provided the possible means of the salvation of humanity. Read this book carefully – it could constitute the Doctor's greatest attempt so far to save us all from the evil of the Daleks.

S E C T I O N

1

KNOW YOUR ENEMY

This section of the *Dalek Survival Handbook* is designed to make you aware of basic Dalek facts and information. The material is gleaned from a variety of sources, as detailed in the introduction to this book.

CROSS-SECTION OF A DALEK

1 The Dalek's eye is mounted on a shaft that allows vertical movement. The Dalek dome can turn through 360 degrees, so all round vision is possible, though as with most species the area immediately behind the Dalek is the main blind spot. The eye scans the visible light spectrum, with options for infra-red or heat-seeking vision, and other advanced functions.

2 In early Daleks, the data from the eye was translated back into visual representations on a screen in the main environment chamber. In the modern Dalek, however, that data is transferred directly into the brain of the Dalek creature and can be analysed by the creature, or by any of the onboard computer systems.

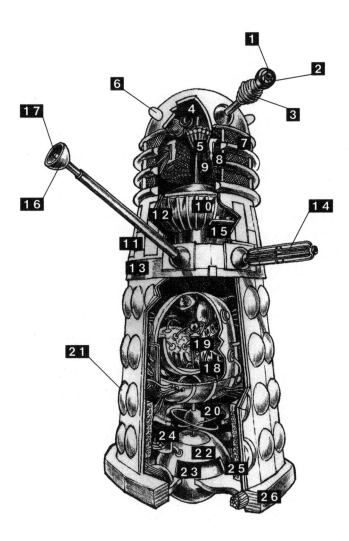

3 The pale blue discs behind the lens serve as physical protection from attack as well as absorbing and assimilating audio data. In effect the Dalek hears through these, sounds being converted using holographic quadraphonic sampling so that directional information as well as estimates of distance and audio-pattern recognition (such as voice print identification) can be appended to the data before it is passed to the Dalek creature.

4 Many of the Dalek machine's main reasoning and computational systems are located inside the dome. These include the communications system and translation unit.

5 The communications system handles local voice projection as well as microwave contact with other Daleks and central control. The translation system has phrase listings and vocabulary banks for every known language and handles simultaneous translation of the Dalek's speech using alpha-wave augmentation to ensure it is understood by anyone within hearing. This system also includes the automatic distress transmitter that sends a warning to the nearest Dalek local command centre if the Dalek is attacked, or its casing is breached.

6 The luminosity dischargers look like light bulbs. These are lit when the Dalek speaks. There are various theories that try to account for this. According to one, excess energy is released through these 'safety valves' but this does not account for the synchronization with the speech circuits. While some documentary evidence does exist that suggests that the lights flash when the Dalek is not speaking, the most plausible theory to date is that the lights simply serve to indicate to other life-forms which Dalek is speaking.

7 Daleks 'eat' by absorbing nutrients from the atmosphere, processing the material, and passing it through to the main environment chamber where the Dalek creature floats in its nutrient-rich liquid. These nutrients, together with atmospheric data, temperature readings, and the background radiation the Dalek needs to sustain it, are absorbed through these mesh or glass screens, then filtered through...

8 ...to a network of storage and filtration systems for processing.

9 The central positronic computer systems augment the Dalek creature's own brain functions and provide back-up processing, information retrieval and storage facilities.

10 The main environment chamber is where the Dalek creature is housed within the casing. Floating in its nutrient-rich fluid, and attached directly by positronic linkages into the various onboard systems, the Dalek is like the commander of a tank. Except that creature and machine are virtually inseparable. It is possible to disconnect and remove the Dalek creature from its environment, but this would only happen in extreme circumstances.

11 The casing of the Dalek is made from an incredibly tough and durable metal called dalekenium. The dalekenium is covered with a polycarbide coating for greater durability and low friction. Despite the apparent density of equipment within the Dalek, the creature can be accessed by Dalek engineers simply by lifting the top, domed section of the Dalek – such is the elegance and functionality of the Dalek's internal design.

12 The empty space within the casing of the Dalek is charged with inert gas that regulates the temperature and other environmental factors. While this serves as excellent insulation, prolonged exposure to extremely cold environments can slow the Dalek's reflexes and, in some circumstances, lead to a state of suspended animation.

13 These power slats absorb sunlight and ambient radiation to be converted into motive power for the Dalek. Note that some models do not have these power slats, in which case they may derive their motive energy from other sources – for example, directly from the metal flooring of the Dalek City, or via an energy collection dish mounted on the Dalek's back which receives energy signals direct from a local transmitter.

14 The Dalek's gun can be set to several levels of destructive capability including 'stun', 'kill' and 'total extermination'.

15 The gun is connected to this small but incredibly powerful energy source. The energy is fed through a ruby crystal array to enhance and focus the energy beam.

16 The sucker cup on the Dalek's arm produces an intensely strong vacuum. Note that this attachment can be exchanged for other appendages dependent upon circumstances. Other Dalek attachments include grabber claw, cutting equipment, preceptor dish, flame-thrower…

17 Inside the sucker cup a slim data rod extends to fit

inside the controls of Dalek equipment such as the transolar disc (also referred to on occasion as a 'hovabout'). Note that later 'Imperial' models of Dalek have a slotted sucker cup to perform this function rather than the protected internal data rod.

18 Command and control systems. This is in effect the Dalek battle computer, which relays strategy assessments and combat data to the other systems and the Dalek Creature.

19 The main Dalek memory banks can store as much information as is held in the British Library.

20 Based on the design of the Dalek anti-gravitational disc, this internal levitation system can raise the Dalek over rough terrain or even up a flight of stairs.

21 These globes function as the external sense organs of the Dalek that are not already catered for (such as the eye). They can detect changes in environmental conditions such as temperature, quality of air and pollution levels, even light intensity and radiation levels. They can detect distant movement beyond visual range by means of SONAR and other advanced Dalek techniques.

2 2 The gyroscopic stabilization system enables the Dalek to remain upright in adverse circumstances. Since the Dalek creature does not 'see' in the conventional sense of the word and obviously has no personal sense of balance, this system serves to indicate basic directional information such as up and down and relate it to the current orientation of the Dalek's casing.

2 3 This is the Dalek's motive power system. It propels the Dalek, and handles changes of direction. In the Dalek City on Skaro, the system picks up power directly from the metal flooring in the form of static electricity. Away from static, electrical power is generated from energy absorbed by the power slats. The generation of this power gives off ozone – which is why Daleks expending a lot of energy smell a little like dodgem cars at a fairground.

2 4 Power storage cells. While the power slats absorb solar energy and power from other sources such as background radioactivity, power is stored for future use in circumstances where an external power source may not be available.

2 5 The base of the Dalek is sealed. The nature of the ground beneath the Dalek (or space, if applicable) is sampled using osmotic retrieval and is constantly analyzed for trace elements. If useful material is detected in the surface, it may be absorbed through the base to provide nutrients, or even power – heat, for example, can be converted to static electrical energy and routed to the power storage cells.

26 One theory for the use of these 'bumpers' is that they detect signals that warn them when other Daleks are dangerously close. It has been claimed that during the Battle of Poseidon, several Dalek battalions were wiped out by their own Daleks. However, since there are no visual records of Daleks without these fenders (even going back to the Ancient Egyptian hieroglyphic evidence), this claim must be treated with a degree of scepticism. It is more likely that they serve much as the bumpers of cars – protecting the Dalek casing from collisions.

RANKS OF THE DALEKS

▇ THE EMPEROR DALEK

Over the centuries reports have come in of various
different Dalek colour schemes and configurations.
Obviously styles and designations change, which
explains any apparent conflict of data.

It also means that despite being compiled from
evidence and records that include information brought
back from the future, the list below may already be out
of date.

★ STAR SYSTEM: Where there is conflicting information,
the alternative sightings and reports are annotated with
a star system – the more stars given to a particular
sighting, the more plausible we believe it to be.

▶ EMPEROR TYPE 1

▷ Sighting reported in vicinity of Sol 3 (Mutters Spiral), 1963AD

★ **OVERALL:** White.

★ **SENSE GLOBES:** Gold.

SHOULDER SLATS: None.

APPENDAGES: None – vision systems linked to letterbox-shaped panel in dome.

NOTES: Large spherical head section. Rumours suggest that this may contain what little remains of the Daleks' originator, Davros.

▶ **EMPEROR TYPE 2**

▷ Sightings from 1960s Annual Reports

★ **OVERALL:** Gold.

SENSE GLOBES: Only three rows, gold.

SHOULDER SLATS: Bands only, no slats. Gold.

APPENDAGES: Eye stalk with red rings and solid white iris, sucker arm, gun.

NOTES: Large spherical head section. Only three rows of Sense Globes. Seven luminosity dischargers arranged round back half of dome/sphere.

▶ **EMPEROR TYPE 3**

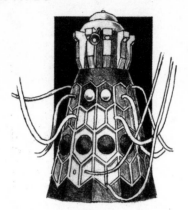

▷ Sighting from investigation of the 'Dalek Factor', Skaro – date unknown

★ **NOTES:** This Emperor Dalek is unlike a standard
★ Dalek. It stands about 30 feet high, and is 'plumbed
★ in' to the corner of a control room within the Dalek City on Skaro. It has an eye stalk, but no other appendages.

2 IN THEIR NATURAL HABITAT

▶ SKARO CITY DALEK

▷ Sightings of Daleks within their City on the planet Skaro

OVERALL: Silver.

SENSE GLOBES: Blue.

SHOULDER SLATS: Silver bands only, no slats.

APPENDAGES: Eye stalk with pale blue rings and solid white iris, sucker arm, gun. Also witnessed: cutting arm in place of sucker arm.

NOTES: Film evidence exists of different models: pale blue with dark blue dome and globes; gold shoulder rings; enlarged base and luminosity dischargers, and mechanical claw in place of sucker arm on some models. These reports also mention a black Dalek Leader with alternate gold and silver globes, and a red Dalek Lieutenant with black globes and gold base.

▶ SKARO CITY DALEK – LATER MODEL

▷ Sightings from Dalek Civil War

OVERALL: Silver.

SENSE GLOBES: Blue.

SHOULDER SLATS: Silver.

APPENDAGES: Eye stalk with blue rings and solid white iris, sucker arm, gun.

NOTES: Section leader Daleks have black dome and shoulder slats. These Daleks did battle with the 'humanized' drone Daleks.

3 DALEK INVASION FORCE

▶ TYPE 1

▷ Sighted invading Earth in 22nd century (version of history 'A')
OVERALL: Silver.
SENSE GLOBES: Blue.
SHOULDER SLATS: Rings only. Silver.
APPENDAGES: Eye stalk with blue rings and solid white iris, sucker arm, gun.
NOTES: Enlarged base for travel over rough terrain. Collection dish on back of Dalek to receive power from relay station.

▶ TYPE 2

▷ Sighted invading Earth in 22nd century (version of history 'B' – film evidence)

OVERALL: Silver.

SENSE GLOBES: Blue.

SHOULDER SLATS: Silver.

APPENDAGES: Eye stalk with blue rings and solid white iris, sucker arm or mechanical claw, gun.

NOTES: Also sighted: gold Chief Dalek with silver shoulder slats and black globes; black Mine Controller with silver shoulder slats and gold globes; red Saucer-Pilot Dalek with silver shoulder slats and globes.

▶ TYPE 3

▷ Sighted invading Earth in 22nd century (version of history 'C')

OVERALL: Black.

SENSE GLOBES: Black.

SHOULDER SLATS: Black.

APPENDAGES: Eye stalk with blue rings and circular white iris with dark centre, sucker arm, gun.

NOTES: Chief Dalek is gold with black globes.

4 STANDARD DALEKS

▶ DALEK DRONE – TYPE 1

▷ Sightings from Dalek Masterplan incident, the Vulcan colony incursion, and unconfirmed reports from England, 1866, as well as various other periods. Possibly also present on Aridius, Mechanus, and other locations

OVERALL: Silver.

SENSE GLOBES: Blue.

SHOULDER SLATS: Silver.

APPENDAGES: Eye stalk with blue rings and solid white iris, sucker arm, gun.

NOTES: Reports of slightly different models, also of use of detection equipment, flame throwers, etc. in place of sucker arm.

▶ DALEK DRONE – TYPE 2

▷ Sightings from early Dalek creation myths, Spiridon incursion, war with the Movellans, liberation of Davros, occupation of Necros, and 1963 Skaro faction Dalek force

OVERALL: Gunmetal grey/black.

SENSE GLOBES: Black.

SHOULDER SLATS: Gunmetal grey or black (several variations).

APPENDAGES: Eye stalk with blue rings and white iris ring, sucker arm, gun.

NOTES: Reports of slightly different models. During the Movellan war, different versions worked within the same battle sections (in varying degrees of disrepair).

▶ DALEK DRONE – TYPE 3

▷ It seems that this version, a variation of Type 1, may be adapted for long-haul space flight. This explains the reflective surfaces that may stave off some of the adverse affects of hyperspatial exposure

OVERALL: Silver.

SENSE GLOBES: Black.

SHOULDER SLATS: Silver, with black 'shoulders' beneath.

APPENDAGES: Eye stalk with blue rings and white iris ring, sucker arm, gun.

NOTES: This model only features in one report concerning the planet Exxilon.

▣ **IMPERIAL DALEKS**

▶ **IMPERIAL DALEK – TYPE 1**

▷ Sighted on the planet Necros at Tranquil Repose, this version of the
Dalek was built by Davros. The Dalek creature inside was mutated
from a prominent human being left in perpetual instatement on
Necros. These Daleks were all destroyed by the Skaro-faction Daleks
loyal to the Dalek Supreme when they captured Davros

OVERALL: Ivory.

SENSE GLOBES: Gold.

SHOULDER SLATS: Gold.

APPENDAGES: Eye stalk with blue rings and white iris
ring, sucker arm, gun.

NOTES: Some observers describe the general colour
scheme as 'cream'. This designation is discouraged by
Daleks.

▶ **IMPERIAL DALEK
– TYPE 2**

▷ Sighted on Earth, 1963 time sector. These Daleks were working for
the Emperor Dalek, although it is thought that this turned out to be
Davros inside the Emperor's casing rather than the real Emperor. (See
Ranks of the Daleks on page 33.)

OVERALL: Ivory.

SENSE GLOBES: Gold.

SHOULDER SLATS: Gold.

APPENDAGES: Eye stalk with blue rings and gold iris
ring, sucker arm, gun.

NOTES: The sucker arm is slotted to fit into Dalek
control systems. The general shape is more angular
with a lozenge-shape embossed on the front section.
Luminosity dischargers differ from the normal
arrangement, being flatter and illuminated in a ring
around the edge. The base is ivory rather than the
usual black.

6 THE DALEK SUPREME

▷ DALEK SUPREME
TYPE 1

▷ Led the invasion of Earth, 2157AD (Version of history 'A')

OVERALL: Black.

SENSE GLOBES: Blue.

SHOULDER SLATS: Rings only. Silver.

APPENDAGES: Eye stalk with blue rings and solid white iris, sucker arm, gun.

NOTES: Enlarged base for travel over rough terrain. Collection dish on back of Dalek to receive power from relay station. Some reports suggest the Dalek Supreme – also known on this occasion as 'The Black Dalek' – had alternate black and silver base sections. This is unconfirmed and it is possible that in fact this was a different Dalek in charge of a Dalek Saucer, and that it was red, rather than black.

▶ DALEK SUPREME TYPE 2

▷ Sighted during the Dalek Masterplan incident

OVERALL: Black.

SENSE GLOBES: Blue.

SHOULDER SLATS: Silver.

APPENDAGES: Eye stalk with blue rings and solid white iris, sucker arm, gun.

NOTES: This Dalek Supreme also features in Space/Time Visualizer material, giving orders on Skaro.

▶ DALEK SUPREME TYPE 3

▷ Sighted invading Earth in 22nd century (version of history 'C')
OVERALL: Gold.
SENSE GLOBES: Black.
SHOULDER SLATS: Gold.
APPENDAGES: Eye stalk with blue rings and circular white iris with dark centre, sucker arm, gun.
NOTES: Never actually referred to as a Dalek Supreme, this may be a sub-commander (sometimes called 'Chief') Dalek.

▶ DALEK SUPREME TYPE 4

▷ Sighted on Spiridon, in the Ninth System, 2540AD

OVERALL: Black, with gold dome.

SENSE GLOBES: Gold.

SHOULDER SLATS: Gold.

APPENDAGES: Eye stalk with blue rings and illuminating iris, sucker arm, gun.

NOTES: Referred to by the Daleks as 'the Dalek Supreme' and by the Thals' expeditionary force as 'one of the Supreme Council'. Enlarged base and luminosity dischargers.

▶ DALEK SUPREME TYPE 5

▷ Sighted on Earth in 1963 commanding 'rebel' Dalek faction

OVERALL: Black.

SENSE GLOBES: Silver.

SHOULDER SLATS: Silver.

APPENDAGES: Eye stalk with blue rings and circular white iris with dark centre, sucker arm, gun.

NOTES: Referred to in contemporary documentation only as 'Black Dalek'. Red luminosity dischargers.

SPECIAL WEAPONS DALEKS

These uber-Daleks originated when, seeking to
execute a renegade, time-travelling faction of their own
race, the Daleks fired what they thought was deadly
radiation at their victims. But this Astro-thesial
radiation, as they called it, had an unexpected effect on
these renegade Daleks. It made them uncontrollably
angry and capable of releasing far higher levels of
psycho-kinetic energy to their weapons. In short, they
were psychopathic killers, even by Dalek standards.

After some years, the Daleks once again tracked
down these renegades, this time imprisoning them.
After massive reconditioning and surgical coercion, the
Daleks managed to implant the renegades inside
reinforced outer shells. They gave them bigger and
better weapons through which to vent their
psychopathic tendencies. It is these reconditioned
renegades that became the Special Weapons Daleks.

Once they had proved their worth in battle during
their spectacular victory at the battle of Cairtros IV,
the Dalek Emperor ordered full-scale reproduction of
these new Daleks. Since then, proliferation of the
Special Weapons Daleks has continued unabated.

KNOWN TYPES IN SERVICE

▶ STANDARD BATTLE
TYPE

The Standard Battle type has been the most widely
encountered Special Weapons Dalek. The Dalek
creature contained in the 'life chamber' of this model
has been reconditioned for total obedience and
minimal independent thought. It relies on its
immediate superior (often nicknamed the 'Minder')
for tactical instructions. In emergency situations, the
Minder can relinquish control, giving the Special
Weapons Dalek autonomy. However, it has been noted
by all forces engaging this model when it is in
autonomous mode, that the end result is usually self-
destruction immediately following the accidental
destruction of any other Daleks in the area. It seems
that a Minder Dalek will only set its underling free
when a battle situation is deemed irretrievable.

Presumably, the Dalek hope is that the uncontrollable Special Weapons Dalek will wreak so much havoc that the outcome will not be a clear victory for either side.

When under control of its Minder, the Standard Battle type's creature often suffers from an overactive schrellic gland. It has been discovered, during dissection of a Dalek creature, that the schrellic gland becomes particularly active when a Dalek is in a battle situation. It excretes a noxious fluid, which is thought to attract the attention of other Daleks, possibly as a petition for reinforcements. In the case of this type of Special Weapons Dalek, the volume of schrellic secretion is such that it often leaks out of the Dalek casing around the gun area. This sticky fluid has often been mistaken for some kind of lubrication oil, although it is by no means certain that the fluid does not fulfil this function as well.

The energy output of the Standard Battle type's gun has been gauged at up to 50 times that of a normal Dalek's not inconsiderably powerful blast.

Schrellic gland secretion
– particularly active
in a battle situation.

▶ AIRBORNE TYPE

The Airborne Special Weapons Dalek is an altogether more sophisticated model. Dalek conditioning techniques for these aggressive renegades had become markedly more advanced by the time these were developed. They are capable of intelligent speech and have interpretative skills when it comes to following orders transmitted on the Dalek command net during intense battle situations. There is even anecdotal evidence to suggest that one Dalek creature who was originally housed within an Airborne Dalek's casing had impressed its superiors to such an extent, that it was relocated into a red Supreme Commander casing.

The Airborne SWD is sleek in design and more aerodynamic than the standard Dalek design. It never settles on the surface of a planet, but instead hovers constantly, eager to put into practice one of its many breath-taking battle manoeuvres.

▶ TORPEDO TYPE

The Torpedo type is so named because of their brief and often fatal encounters with this underwater version of the Special Weapons Dalek. First sighted in the initial battles on the largely ocean-covered planet Guria, this type of Dalek was indeed initially mistaken for a submarine torpedo. Not surprisingly, since at first sight it both looks and travels like a torpedo. However, capture and analysis of this type revealed its cunning adaptability.

Equipped with an advanced caterpillar drive (the underwater equivalent of a jet engine) and packed with formidable power reserves, it is more than a match for any military submarine. The ingenuity of its design however, allows its outer casing to react with seawater in order to temporarily alter the molecular structure of the bonded polycarbide shell. The nature of the structure is governed by an onboard menu of molecules stored in the Dalek's battle computer. The result is that this Special Weapons Dalek can assume the appearance, texture and feel of a rock on the seabed or a log floating in the water, for example. In situations of dire emergency, it can actually become a torpedo. This Dalek is preconditioned to sacrifice itself with maximum explosive force should the situation call for it.

■ COMBAT RECORD

When the Special Weapons Daleks were first deployed, their impact was immense. Commanders would incorrectly assess long range scans of Dalek troop movements, interpreting Special Weapons Daleks as normal Daleks. In these situations, forces committed to a battle would inevitably be pitifully inadequate in number and firepower. There were many bloody massacres.

Little by little, however, the full extent of the power of the Special Weapons Daleks was revealed. It was not long before opposing forces were fighting back with a vengeance.

▶ TOP FIVE SPECIAL WEAPONS VICTORIES

1 STERAXIUS: A flotilla of Torpedo Daleks posed as a shoal of beached water mammals in distress. As the Steraxian Ecological Foundation operatives approached them, the Torpedoes opened fire, devastating a large proportion of the planet's defences, leaving Steraxius open to Dalek conquest.

2 THE JUNGLE PLANET OF JUNGLOS (so named by the first, rather unimaginative pioneers to discover the planet): A mere four Airborne Special Weapons

Daleks kept an entire division of troops confused and besieged in the tropical jungles for months. The troops eventually ran out of rations and died of starvation.

3 CAIRTROS IV: General Arthur Brook had no intelligence information about Special Weapons Daleks. Long range scans indicated the presence of 50 Daleks. Brook allocated a force of 300 men, thought sufficient to take care of such a small force of Daleks. On landing, the 300 men were reduced to zero in less than five minutes.

4 MISCYAM: A squadron of Airborne Daleks was mistaken for the return of the mystical Flying Gods of MiscYam legends, with apocalyptic consequences for the indigenous life-forms.

5 THE HAND OF OMEGA AFFAIR: In this instance a single standard-model Imperial Special Weapons Dalek (second class) was responsible for the defeat of an entire renegade Dalek task force. The Special Weapons Dalek concerned was cited for an award for 'Extreme Extermination in the Face of Danger'. Unfortunately it was unable to attend the ceremony, as the Stellar Manipulator it was responsible for capturing accidently manipulated Skaro's sun and wiped out the entire Imperial Dalek faction. Instead, it

was granted a posthumous award for 'services inadvertently rendered' by the surviving renegade Daleks.

▶ TOP FIVE SPECIAL WEAPONS DEFEATS

1 OCEANARON – THE SEA MOON OF KELADOS: A low-level chemical weapon bombing raid transformed the planetoid's oceans into highly corrosive acid, thus destroying the flotilla of Torpedo Daleks who had not-so-cunningly disguised themselves as rather large floating mounds of Dalek-shaped Keladon gull dung.

2 THE GARAZONE CAMPAIGN: Scientists cleverly synthesized the schrellic gland's secretions, luring 50 squadrons of interplanetary Airborne Daleks into a trap. The potency of the schrellic substitute was such that the first 27 squadrons willingly flew into the Garazone sun.

3 THE AKG04 SABOTAGE GAMBIT: An operative, still only known as AKG04 for security reasons, managed to isolate the command frequencies of the Logril 9 Dalek Division's Standard SWD Minders. For several years, this enabled the selective transmitting of false and contradictory commands to Special Weapons

Daleks. Famous amongst these commands were: 'You are very tired – shut down for a short sleep', 'What was that noise behind you?' and 'Human beings are now your friends, cease firing'. The Dalek Supreme ultimately had the frequencies altered and issued orders for conditioning of Special Weapons Daleks to include the annihilation of concepts such as tiredness, friendship and curiosity.

4 **HANDROZ ASTEROID BELT:** A vast force of Special Weapons Daleks was detected hiding in this asteroid belt. Gravitraction stasis mines were used to crush the entire belt to the size of a small refrigeration unit.

5 **LOPRA MINOR:** The final assault by the Knight of Velyshaa Kalendorf, commanding Earth Alliance forces aboard Battlecruiser Courageous. Armed with information gleaned straight from the Dalek command net, a nest of attacking Airborne Special Weapons Daleks was wiped out by sub-orbital assault craft.

▶ **SWD STRENGTHS**

1 **Massive firepower**

2 **Ruthlessness**

3 **Manoeuvrability**

4 **Terrifying appearance**

5 **Camouflage** (Torpedo Daleks only)

▶ **SWD WEAKNESSES**

1 **Over-aggressive** if not controlled by Minder

2 **Lacking sophistication,** hence the old expression, 'As stupid as an SWD'

3 **Relatively short lifespan**

4 **Over-productive schrellic gland** sometimes causes internal drowning

5 **Occasional conditioning lapses** causing petulant disobedience

HOW TO SURVIVE ENFORCED CAPTIVITY WITH A DALEK

Following the collapse of a large Dalek mineworks at the end of a hostile Dalek occupancy of Earth, a series of systematic excavations were carried out. The hope was that Dalek technology left behind could be reclaimed for the good of the planet's resurrection.

The work was dangerous, but proceeded apace. Often the team of selfless volunteers would go into dire peril; many were crushed by falling rock, suffocated by pockets of gas, or else fell down big holes they failed to notice in the dark. But the greatest danger lay in the fact that, sometimes, living Daleks were discovered in the dark tunnels and pits.

Below is a list of useful tips, gleaned from their experiences, for survival when caught with a Dalek in close quarters. The techniques are especially useful on planets with frequent catacombs, pot-holes and/or lifts.

WHAT TO DO WHEN TRAPPED IN AN ENCLOSED SPACE WITH A DALEK

Ⓐ SWIFTLY ASSESS THE SITUATION

1 WHAT IS YOUR STATUS? Much depends on how both of you came to be in the enclosed space. Did you fall into a hole from some height? Check swiftly for injuries. If you are shielded by fallen rock or similar, carry out first aid on cuts, gashes and bruises using material from your clothing as bandages. If you are in plain view, attempt to reach cover swiftly before attempting contact with the Dalek. If you try to run but can't, your legs may be broken.

2 WHAT IS THE DALEK'S STATUS? Did the Dalek also fall some distance? Check its posture to help assess its threat. This guide may be helpful:

■ Unthreatening.

■ Quite threatening.
Be vigilant and take
cover if possible.

■ Life-threatening.
Take immediate
evasive action.

3 **WHAT IS YOUR LOCATION?** It is important to know where you are in order to assess how easy it will be to escape your situation. Will others be looking for you? This will be of great assistance. Will other Daleks be looking for the Dalek? This will probably be less helpful.

4 **HOW LONG HAS THE DALEK BEEN HERE?** A simple visual check is usually sufficient to gauge this.

This Dalek has been a prisoner some time.

This Dalek is a new arrival.

Ⓑ COMMENCE CONTACT WITH THE DALEK

1 DO NOT waste time attempting lengthy introductions or enquiring as to the Dalek's welfare. Daleks are notoriously uninterested in smalltalk, and will exterminate you.

2 DO NOT beg the Dalek not to kill you, or to give you protection, etc. The Dalek will remain unmoved by even the most heartfelt pleas and exterminate you.

3 DO NOT attempt to threaten or cajole the Dalek into giving assistance. The Dalek will shortly take umbrage and exterminate you and probably anyone else present.

4 DO speak calmly and with authority. Explain to the Dalek that you can be of assistance to it, and that by working together you can both escape. IT IS OF VITAL IMPORTANCE to convince the Dalek SWIFTLY that you are necessary to its achieving freedom/continued existence. A good point to make is that you can climb and scale rocks in order to benefit the Dalek (unless your legs are broken – see point A 1). REMEMBER – the Dalek is not enjoying being stuck in a hole any more than you are.

© ASSESS LIKELIHOOD OF RESCUE

1 SCOUT OUT IMMEDIATE ENVIRONS: Having convinced the Dalek of your viability as a partner in any escape attempt, you must now survey the scene. It is likely that the Dalek will already have attempted a survey but PERFORM YOUR OWN REGARDLESS AND TAKE NOTHING ON TRUST. The Dalek may be telling the truth, but it may also be hiding information from you to its own advantage.

THE CEILINGS IN THE VICINITY ARE STRUCTURALLY SOUND

Conclusion: The Dalek's appearance here suggests a lie.

Conclusion: The Dalek's appearance here suggests a lie.

Conclusion: The Dalek's immediate environs here suggest a lie.

Conclusion: The Dalek's appearance full stop suggests it is telling the truth. But do not take its use of the word 'we' to necessarily include yourself.

2 **LOCATE POSSIBLE EXITS:** Having banded together with the Dalek, you must now co-operate in order to find an exit. It is vital you unite as equal allies. After all, although the Dalek brings its armoured shell (with battering ram possibilities) and heavy-duty blasting gear in the form of its gun stick to the table, you bring the ability to move small rocks out of its way. NB. RESIST ALL EFFORTS ON THE DALEK'S PART TO ADOPT A MORE SENIOR ROLE IN YOUR PARTNERSHIP – unless danger of death is imminent. Remember that Daleks often enslave lesser races purely out of habit.

ⓓ PROCEED WITH CAUTION

■ ALWAYS proceed along tunnels BEHIND or
ALONGSIDE the Dalek. This will reduce your
chances of accidental extermination considerably.

ⓔ THE WAKING ALLY

Daleks do not need rest. You therefore may find it
necessary to repose upon the Dalek while it continues
the search for escape. In her pamphlet 'Sleeping with
Daleks and Waking Refreshed', the exotic miner
Francine 'Minah-bird' Mole (who once travelled for
13 days and nights on the back of a Dalek along an
underground mine shaft on Kemble) recommends
certain positions:

1 **BRIDE OF SACRIFICE**
As well as proving quite comfortable, all extremities are well clear of Dalek manipulation. Ms Mole recommended this for invalids or 'those not willing to open their minds to extreme possibilities'.

2 **RIDER FROM SHANG-TU**
Not only does this position allow for no possibility of the Dalek shooting or dropping you, it is ideal for keeping the feet dry in waterlogged conditions. Ms Mole also derived some strange comfort from hugging something 'so unyielding and proud' in her distressing journey.

3 THE SEA BEGGAR
Again, the Dalek's extremities can not be trained on you but can be held by the rider for security, and Ms Mole reported 'a feeling of exhilarating empowerment through gripping the Dalek's weapon'.

4 THE WATCHER
In this position, for advanced yogis only, Ms Mole reported the psychological benefits of 'placing oneself atop the Dalek's dome… gaining… an ecstatic sense of dominance over the alien aggressor'. Not recommended in areas with low ceilings.

ⓕ BE VIGILANT

Often, entombed humans and Daleks, entirely focused
on the seriousness of their plight, miss vital clues to
obtaining release from their predicament. The keen-
eyed should watch out for these tell-tale signs that
point to possible freedom:

This implies that an exit is at
hand. Your situation counts
as an emergency so you can
proceed through it with
impunity. The possibility of
stairs is to be welcomed as a

chance of putting distance between you and the Dalek.

Report to the Dalek
immediately upon sighting the
ladder that you can see a
platform large enough for a
Dalek to stand on together
with ropes and pulleys waiting
just at its top. The Dalek will
be suspicious but may allow
you to climb and fetch it. If
the ladder leads to an escape
route, take it immediately at

speed. If the ladder leads nowhere, descend and apologize convincingly to the Dalek for your mistake.

▦ Never miss the obvious. This door may lead to an escape route. Note that Dalek sucker arms are not well suited to small fiddly tasks such as sliding bolts and so your humanoid form presents an advantage.

However, be very sure of what lies beyond before triumphantly racing through and shutting the Dalek outside. If you see any of the following behind the door, retreat immediately –

– and attempt to excuse yourself to the Dalek, which may have taken umbrage and so wish to exterminate you.

■ Do not be mistrustful of the obvious. All life-forms labouring in catacombs appreciate clear signage pointing the way out. If the Dalek insists on leading the way out, DO NOT FOLLOW – as it may exterminate you upon reaching freedom. If possible, once free, simulate your death by dropping a heavy rock on the floor and screaming briefly.

N.B. Wait some considerable time before emerging to ensure the Dalek HAS GONE.

ⓖ THE AFTERMATH

After an enforced period of entrapment, with long dark days spent in shared camaraderie with a Dalek, many humans who lived to tell the tale reported feelings of deep emotional attachment to their Dalek companions. Francine 'Minah Bird' Mole in particular embraced 'the love that dare not speak its name', and, after eight years of pining and petitioning the Kemble authorities, was allowed to visit the Dalek that had won her heart during their shared ordeal, without the presence of guards.

Ms Mole was shortly exterminated.

SIGHTING PROCEDURE – WHAT TO DO IF YOU SEE A DALEK

If you do see a Dalek, it is your duty to inform the authorities at the earliest opportunity. There are a number of ways you can do this:

- Use one of the emergency security telephones. These are housed in blue boxes at strategic locations. Security Officers and armoured cars respond to all calls (pull to open).

- Call the Emergency Number (020 8433 1244) from any phone.

- Fill in form DS-159/G-1, which is available from your local Post Office. This form will ask you the following questions, so have the answers ready:
  - Date and time of sighting
  - Location
  - Your name, address, contact details and security ident code (if applicable – if you don't know what this is, then you don't have one)
  - Whether you have previously reported sightings that were discovered to be false alarms (tick the appropriate box for '1–5', '5–10', 'More than 10')

☐ Number and types of Dalek(s) sighted

☐ Names of other witnesses who can corroborate (note, it is obviously helpful if these people are still alive after the Dalek Event)

☐ Brief description of the circumstances and what happened

☐ Your next of kin

(Note that the section headed 'Is the Witness still Living' is for office use only, and you should not attempt to fill in this section of the form.)

Other points to bear in mind if you sight a Dalek:

▪ Do *not* approach the Dalek or attempt to arrest it yourself. This can be extremely hazardous.

▪ Make *no* sudden movements or loud noises (for example, screams, unless simulating death – see page 75) that might alert the Dalek to your presence.

▪ Do *not* attempt to engage the Dalek in conversation or distract it in some way to give the Security Forces time to arrive.

▪ Keep *well away* from the area where the Dalek is, but make yourself available to the Security Commander when he or she arrives on the scene.

If in doubt, running away from the Dalek is usually a good strategy.

Note that in the event of discovering the site of a previous Dalek attack, you should be prepared to give a full statement to the Scene of Extermination Officer.

DEATH TO THE DALEKS – BASIC TIPS TO FULFILLING YOUR GOAL

The reaction of the average human subject when unexpectedly faced with a Dalek is complete terror. The Dalek is, after all, heavily armoured, pitiless and extremely aggressive, whereas the average human civilian is soft, easily surprised and often confused when confronted with something out of the ordinary.

However, for all their military might, there have been suggestions in the past that Daleks do have certain weak points. Should you find yourself confronted by a Dalek, with no hiding place and with surrender or flight not an option, you may be able to use one or more of the following tips to mitigate the desperation of your position.

DALEK WEAK POINTS

1 THE EYE STALK
The flexible shaft holding the Dalek's single bulbous eye could be a target. It is slender and, for a Dalek, quite delicate. A saw, or, in dire circumstances, a club

could be enough to break it off. Never attempt to snap it with your bare hands.

If you have no appropriate weapon to hand, you could try throwing mud at the lens. This will disable the Dalek's vision, allowing you to escape, or attack the Dalek further. (N.B. Always use wet mud, since dry earth will not stick. If the Dalek has given you a particular fright you may well find the mud at your feet very wet indeed.)

2 OUTER CASING

There are rumoured to be chinks in a Dalek's polycarbide armour. A small area in the ball joint of the gunstick may be vulnerable to bullets, though a successful attack by this means would require careful aim and skilled marksmanship. This aside, the outer casing seems particularly vulnerable to bombs of various types. N.B. Do not be complacent if you possess a bomb when confronted by a Dalek. Actual efficacy of bombs varies considerably from case to case. Generally, the larger the explosion the greater the chance of Dalek injury, but one should never assume total success – after having set your bomb, do not remain in the vicinity in the hope of celebrating your enemy's demise, but retreat at once. You are thus at least taking advantage of any temporary disorientation you may have engendered.

3 EXTREME CHANGES IN TEMPERATURE

Being heavily armoured, Daleks do not generally notice changes in the weather. However, sudden extremes of temperature variation can occasionally give Daleks fatal shocks. This is a risky stratagem that rarely works in temperate climates and there are very few reports of success.

If you are attacked on a boiling hot day, and happen to have access to a large freezing cold puddle, obscure the Dalek's eye as per weak point 1, and shove it in for a fatal soaking. On freezing cold days, look for hot tar pits, volcanic mud baths or lava blowholes in the immediate area.

4 MOTIVE POWER

Depending on their date of origin, some Daleks use solar dishes that harness sunlight as a power source for their motive units. Other Daleks are reliant on static electricity to propel themselves along metal surfaces. Such Daleks can be easily detected and attacked.

For attacks on metal surfaces, push Dalek on top of heavy fabric (ideally a non-conductive, insulating cloak lent to you by the leader of an alien race) to disable its motive power.

For attacks on sunny days, ascertain if Dalek has a dish on its back, and, if it has, use any means available to keep the dish in shadow for long enough to drain

the Dalek of energy. (This could take some time.)
(N.B. 99 per cent of Daleks, unfortunately, run on
batteries and so are entirely self-sufficient. Be wary of
attempting to exploit this occasional weakness unless
all else has failed.)

S E C T I O N

2

SUPPLEMENTARY DATA

This section provides detailed information about all aspects of the Dalek race, as gathered from sources in the past, present and even from the future (see *Introduction*).

THE CREATION OF THE DALEKS

▷ Because of the revealing nature of the information this transcript contains, it is presented here in its entirety. No information is available as to the date or provenance of the material, but UNIT analysts believe the contents to provide vital insight into the creation of the Daleks.

CONFLICTING HISTORIES: THE CREATION MYTHS

The single most controversial aspect of Dalek history is the matter of their genesis, and the clear cause of the controversy surrounding the genesis of the Daleks is conflicting information from different sources. The sources are as follows:

1 THE DALEK CHRONICLES: discovered and translated by Terry Nation.

2 THE TIME LORD ARCHIVES: specifically, accounts of the activities of 'The Doctor'.

3 THE BRYANT ANDERSON REPORT: fragments recovered from a covert mission to the planet Ollendorf 2, decoded by Terry Nation and presented in *We Are The Daleks*.

▶ THE DALEK CHRONICLES

When Terry Nation first discovered and translated the *Chronicles*, it was thought that they contained the definitive early history of the Daleks. Some eminent figures still argue, with some justification, that this is the case. However, others have cast doubt upon the nature of these chronicles.

They tell the story of how, on the planet Skaro, the peaceful Thals, native to the continent of Davius, were caught up in a war with the inhabitants of their neighbouring continent, Dalazar. The squat, goblin-like people of Dalazar were known as the Daleks. In the first segment of the chronicles they are on the brink of totally annihilating the Thals with a 'mighty neutron bomb'.

The chronicles depict Dalek War Minister Zolfian's ruthless assassination of the pacifist Dalek leader Drenz. Setting about finding a way to destroy any Thals that might be lucky enough to survive the upcoming neutron bomb attack, Zolfian apparently commissioned his chief scientist, Yarvelling, to develop a powerful war machine. In the images decoded by Nation, this war machine clearly resembles a Dalek.

Zolfian orders the mass production of these war machines, but a mere two weeks later Skaro is hit by a freak 'meteorite storm'. This storm penetrates the Daleks' city defences and sets off the many neutron bombs under construction. The resultant blast turns Skaro into a radioactive wasteland.

Two years later, miraculously surviving, Zolfian and Yarvelling emerge from the ruins of their war chamber. They are confronted by one of their war machines, but it can now speak, and claims to be inhabited by a Dalek creature mutated by the neutron radioactivity. It urges Zolfian and Yarvelling to build more machines to house its fellow mutants ('We cannot… We are all brain,' it explains). The two surviving humanoid Daleks are happy to oblige, seeing this as a way of perpetuating their dreams of Dalek conquest.

By the time of their deaths, Zolfian and Yarvelling have created a golden Dalek Emperor, using flidor gold, quartz and arkellis flower sap. But now the

Daleks need new workers to create more Dalek machines. This need marks the beginning of their aggression against species alien to themselves.

▶ THE TIME LORD ARCHIVES

The most significant archive entry regarding this subject details a Celestial Intervention Agency covert operation to tamper with the timeline in order to prevent the Daleks from becoming a major, destructive influence in the history of the universe. The agency coerced the renegade 'Doctor' into undertaking a mission to prevent the creation of the Daleks, or affect their development so that they might become less aggressive creatures.

However, the Skaro encountered by the Doctor and his human travelling companions bears only a passing resemblance to the one depicted in the *Dalek Chronicles*. In this account, the humanoids fighting the Thals are called Kaleds. There is no Zolfian or Yarvelling, instead the instigator of the creation of the Daleks is a disabled scientist called Davros.

Davros has predicted the ultimate mutation of his race and sets about creating a travel machine to house such a creature. In tandem with this project, he is genetically anticipating this Kaled mutation by creating it under laboratory conditions. Housing these creatures in mechanical travel machines, he elects to name them with an anagram of his race's name... Dalek. He orders a mere 20 of these Daleks to wipe out the entire Thal race while the Thals are celebrating victory, having recently launched a devastating rocket attack on the Kaleds' domed city.

The unwitting Doctor is largely unsuccessful in his mission, only managing to trap the prototype Daleks inside Davros's bunker and destroy the genetic laboratories where more Dalek mutants are being created. Before he leaves Skaro, the Doctor witnesses the Daleks apparently exterminating their creator. Davros had attempted to shut down the Daleks' automated production line, and this could not be tolerated by the Daleks.

It is also worth taking note of an earlier entry in the Time Lord Archive. The entry details the Doctor's first encounter with the Daleks, in which he meets the Thals at some unspecified time after the neutron war that resulted in the creation of the Daleks.

Here, the Doctor studies the Thal race's own historical records, learning that there was a terrible war between the Thals and a race called Dals. The Dals were apparently scholars and philosophers. The Thals were ruthless warriors. Since the war, both races underwent a mutation process brought about by neutron radiation. The Thals mutated into pacifist, elegant humanoids. The Dals mutated into warlike, aggressive non-humanoid creatures which need travel machines in order to survive... the Daleks.

▶ THE BRYANT ANDERSON REPORT

Bryant Anderson was an eminent if unconventional scientist commissioned by Earth's security high command to discover fatal weaknesses in the Daleks by studying their very nature. Much to his alarm, his research led him to discover the case of the Halldons and their experiment with a kidnapped selection of early *homo sapiens* from Earth's pre-history.

Relocating this small community to the planet Ameron, the Halldons took it upon themselves to accelerate the development of human kind in an environment exactly replicating that of Earth. After only a few centuries, the humans on Ameron reached a high enough level of technological proficiency to destroy their captors. With their evolution now accelerating unchecked, Anderson asserts that the humans on Ameron eventually developed into Daleks.

Without further elaboration, Terry Nation made this point in the emotive title of his essay, 'We are the Daleks'. The implied hypothesis is that the Daleks we fight today are the descendants of those who evolved on Ameron and that we, one day, will evolve into Daleks.

ANALYSIS OF THE REPORTS

On the face of it, these varying accounts seem mutually exclusive. However, the key to understanding this is the context and the origin of each piece of evidence.

Unfortunately, almost nothing is known of how the *Dalek Chronicles* were discovered and translated. Although undeniably a man of fierce intellect and integrity, Nation took the secret of his genius to his grave. No one can ascertain the reason for this secrecy, and so therefore no one knows the true source of the *Dalek Chronicles*.

Some say that a number of 'story cubes' were recovered from the wreckage of a Dalek craft. Others assert that they are ancient records made by the Daleks themselves. The truth is, we simply don't know. But if this evidence was recorded by the Daleks, there is no reason to assume that it is true. Our undisputed experience of the Daleks' behaviour is that they regard lies and half-truth as expedient methods of gaining their ends when, for whatever reason, the options of conquest, subjugation and brute force are not available to them.

There is also the possibility that these chronicles are not the work of the Daleks. Another race may be responsible for this history of the genesis of the Daleks, with their own motives for presenting it as they do.

The *Dalek Chronicles'* portrayal of the Daleks' ancestors tends to represent them as not only morally bankrupt, but somewhat inept as well. For example, when our two rather pathetic Dalek figures, Zolfian and Yarvelling emerge from their bunker, they have no idea whether it is safe or not to do so. The supposed genius scientist Yarvelling merely says, 'We must chance it. If we spend another day in that hovel, we shall go mad'. One might argue that they have already gone mad. They know their planet has been devastated by radioactive material. 'Chancing' a stroll on the surface does not seem the action of a rational being.

The narrative flavour of the *Dalek Chronicles* suggests folklore, legend or myth rather than factual, historical account. On the other hand, it may be that this 'myth' is based on hard facts, but given that the evidence from the Time Lord Archive and the *Bryant Anderson Report* is far more detailed, perhaps we should look to these for a more accurate picture.

From the little that is known about the Time Lords, we have gathered that they are a secretive and sometimes devious people. The extracts from their archives have more often than not been obtained through dubious third parties. However, the credibility of the Time Lord evidence is supported by its sheer volume and its detail. The Doctor has had many encounters with the Daleks; a large number of these involving Davros. None of them mentions Zolfian or Yarvelling, who exist as the central characters in the *Chronicles*. What is more, the sociological detail present in this evidence on the Daleks' genesis is far nearer cool historical account than the fantastical tale of two sole survivors bringing about the creation of the galaxy's most feared aggressors.

The inconsistencies in this story, involving the Thals' historical account of the Dals mutating from pacifists into warmongers can perhaps be best explained by the fact that this version is based on line drawings apparently scratched into hexagonal metal plates. This Thal history is arguably as much a legend as the *Dalek Chronicles* story.

One might more sensibly attack the Time Lord evidence on a few small areas of incredibility. Even given the Daleks' known ferocity, is it really likely that Davros expected only 20 of them to wipe out the entire Thal race? Could the wheelchair-bound Davros, with only the help of his sadistic accomplice Nyder, really make their way alone across the war-torn wasteland between the Kaled and Thal domes? And why is it that if there really were 20 of them, so much of the pictographic evidence shows no more than three Daleks present at any one time?

It is clear to see that even this detailed body of evidence has its potential flaws, and we now move on to our last, and perhaps most problematic source.

Bryant Anderson's report corroborates very little of what we have examined so far. He does not mention Zolfian, Yarvelling, Davros or even Skaro, instead locating the genesis of these most inhuman creatures much closer to home – with our own ancestors. But why?

The key question we must ask is, what was Anderson looking for when he took the top off that Dalek on planet Ollendorf 2? Unquestionably, all humanoid species have many physiological and biological similarities. In his analysis of the Dalek mutant creature, did he discover something that could only have been specific to human beings from Earth or merely specific to the generic humanoid form found in our galaxy?

Did Anderson, in his anxiety to warn us of the danger of our own increasingly belligerent tendencies, make a link specifically to our own *homo sapiens* species, that could just as easily have been made to Zolfian's Daleks, or Davros's Kaleds: both equally humanoid?

It may be that all sophisticated humanoid species run the risk of allowing themselves to develop into a Dalek-like race. This said, it may be pointed out that whatever its veracity, or usefulness as an historical source, Bryant Anderson's report may serve as a warning to us all.

SKARO – PLANET OF THE DALEKS

▷ From the *Dalek Chronicles* and from various other sources of information, it is possible to provide a brief overview of the history, geography, and inhabitants of the Dalek planet, Skaro.

▉ LOCATION

Skaro is the 12th planet in its solar system, and the only one capable of supporting life. The original intelligent inhabitants of Skaro, the Kaleds and the Thals, believed that there were only seven galaxies in the universe, and that no other life-supporting planets existed.

▉ HISTORY

The conflicting theories surrounding the creation of the Daleks are covered elsewhere in this book. But certainly the early Daleks believed that over 500 years previously there were two races on this planet: the Kaleds (who became the Daleks), and the Thals. After a massive neutronic war that raged for centuries, the Daleks' forefathers retired into their city surrounded by their travel machines.

Protected from the effects of the war in their underground city, the Daleks believed that most of the Thals had perished in the war. But that there were some survivors, disgustingly mutated survivors, but survivors nonetheless.

According to Thal records, Skaro was once a great world – a perpetual renaissance of art and invention. In one day it was all destroyed.

THE THALS

Before the war, the Thals were a race of warriors and the Daleks' ancestors, the Kaleds, were teachers and philosophers.

After the war the Thals that survived managed to cultivate small plots of land, becoming farmers. But they were forced to rely on a sporadic rainfall that only occurred about every four or five years.

After the great war, most of the Thals died and the survivors mutated. But, unlike that of the Daleks, the Thals' mutation came full circle, refining itself over hundreds of years into the tall, slim, blond human beings that the Thals have become.

Now the Thals have evolved into a race of pacifists, absolutely morally opposed to conflict, although there are reports that they organize resistance against the Daleks both on Skaro and on other planets.

■ THE DALEK CITY

The Dalek City on Skaro is the centre of Dalek
operations. It is the home of the Emperor and from
his chamber deep in the bowels of the city he monitors
and controls the war effort. Information suggests that
this is the third City to occupy this site. The original
domed city was destroyed during the neutronic wars,
the subsequent city by the Monstrons. The current city
is the most impressive yet.

The City is located on the continent of Dalazar and,
as with most Dalek structures, the bulk of the city lies
underground. Its natural defences are formidable. The
Drammankin mountains shield the city from two sides
and the Lake of Mutations prevents access to the city
from the South. The other side faces the Petrified
Jungle.

It is from this lake that huge pipelines feed water to
the reactor complex at the bottom level of the city.
This route is left unguarded by the Daleks as they
believe that the creatures that live in the lake provide
adequate protection.

The city is made entirely of metal, and while inside
the Daleks pick up static electrical power through the
floor – an efficient and ingenious way of disseminating
motive energy.

The reactors that supply this power and all the city's
other energy requirements occupy the lowest levels of

the city, and since the Daleks already possess casings that guard against fallout, it is likely that radiation levels within the city are dangerously high.

Directly above the reactor chamber is the Hydroponic centre. Here vast greenhouses contain flora from all corners of the galaxy, while huge banks of artificial sunlight generators are suspended from the ceiling. It appears that these greenhouses provide the basis of the Daleks' nourishment – plant matter is ground into a fine powder and dispersed through the city by means of air ducts, the Daleks absorbing the 'food' through their outer casings.

The central section of the city contains the Supreme Council Chamber where the Dalek elders meet. On the same level as the council chamber is the Master Control Room, the nerve centre of the Dalek Empire. In here, the city's vital systems are checked and rechecked, and the position and movement of every Dalek is noted and transmitted to the Emperor.

THE PETRIFIED JUNGLE

White and ashen, and veiled by a heavy mist, a traveller's first thought on seeing the petrified jungle is that there has recently been a massive forest fire. The heat from which was obviously incredible – the soil itself is merely sand and ashes. It appears as though the jungle took the initial blast from the first series of neutronic bomb blasts and was instantly petrified.

The trees are like brittle stone which crumbles when touched, and incredibly a few tulip-like flowers were preserved. These are even more delicate than the branches and twigs, though the petals have retained some of their original colour.

THE LAKE OF MUTATIONS

The Lake of Mutations lies behind the Dalek city. According to the Thals, there is some sort of chemical in the water that makes it glow in the moonlight.

The lake itself is the home to hideous mutations, bred and crossbred until the original species have long been forgotten.

ROBOMEN

'From the ashes, an unexpected sign of hope…'
(Quotation from Terel Karan's Post Apocalypse Analysis
2167)

After the Daleks had made their devastating attack
upon our planet Earth in the year 2157AD (diverting
the solar trajectories of meteors to impact upon our

once proud land masses; launching plague-carrying missiles which decimated our populations, and levelling vast urban areas with space-to-planet destronic torpedoes), the survivors of our race expected nothing but final destruction from the metallic invaders. As the first transolar discs and interplanetary saucers touched down, resistance was half-hearted and poorly organized. What, after all, was the use of fighting now? How could mere flesh and blood hope to triumph against the implacable, armoured enemy, apparently utterly ruthless in its intention to exterminate humanity?

Surprisingly, it was the Daleks' introduction of a new and degrading technique of subjugation that was to give the great thinkers of Earth's beleaguered freedom fighters their first inkling of hope. As the choking dust clouds settled, the Daleks did not begin the expected onslaught. Meticulously, almost surgically, they extracted from the human community what they needed for the first part of their audacious, diabolical plan. Prisoners.

ROBOTIZATION
Those unlucky souls who were forced into the Dalek ships during those early days had no way of knowing that the horror of 'robotization' awaited them.

Plundering the shared languages of our planet for a name for this ghastly process, the Daleks took a word that had come to mean 'servant' or even 'friend' and plunged directly to its root meaning, from the Czech verb 'robotit', meaning in modern Earth language 'to drudge' or 'to work without reward'. Indeed, the only reward for those who had been robotized, the Robomen, was ultimately self-destruction.

But it was the fact that the Daleks clearly required surviving humans for their purposes that made the freedom fighters realize that all was not lost. They needed us. They didn't just want to destroy us... at least, not yet.

▶ THE PROCESS

The process of robotization was technologically crude but bluntly effective. After an initial processing and desensitizing of the cerebral functions, the victim was then subjected to brutal surgery. A positronic amplification disc was grafted to the skull, and various low-grade

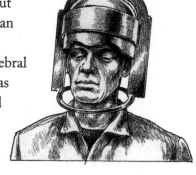

Preparation for robotization.

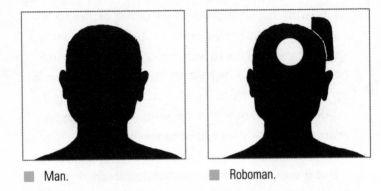

■ Man.   ■ Roboman.

communications hardware attached. The resultant appearance bore none of the sleek hallmarks of the most impressive Dalek scientific achievements, but it served its purpose. The Daleks had created human guard dogs who responded without question, albeit often sluggishly, to spoken or transmitted commands.

The lifespan of these Robomen was short. Some survived for a few years, but most only lived a scant few months under the mind control of the Daleks. The process was irreversible and caused wholesale destruction of brain cells. Some would experience cerebral haemorrhages and collapse. Most would suffer uncontrollable feelings of despair and purposelessness. They would seek the closest route to death, throwing themselves into rivers, off buildings, or impaling themselves on the nearest sharp object protruding from the apocalyptic wreckage that littered the landscape.

Just one of many ways to end your life as a Dalek slave.

But terrifying and demoralizing though the appearance of the Robomen was to the human survivors, they were an indication that the Daleks might have a weakness. They needed human beings to complete their task on Earth. Whether it was slave labour or Robomen they needed, they weren't entirely self-sufficient.

As Terel Karan, the historian who lived through those bleak times, often said, 'For the first time, we dared to think that the Daleks might not be invincible.'

TERRIFYING NEW DEVELOPMENTS

Unfortunately, technology and learning do not stand still for the Daleks. Latest reports, relating to the Dalek incursion that began in the Vega System, indicate that, although the 'traditional' method of robotization is still in evidence, new and more sophisticated techniques have been developed by the Daleks.

New reports state that more meticulous programming and preparation of Robomen has led to them being

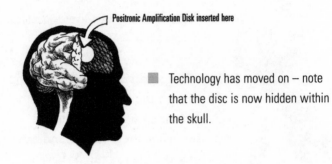

Positronic Amplification Disk inserted here

Technology has moved on – note that the disc is now hidden within the skull.

undetectable and far deadlier. In these models the positronic amplification disc is smaller and is surgically implanted into the brain. It establishes Dalek protocols and priorities in the subject's everyday thought processes, but allows the subject to, largely, continue behaving as a normal human being. This enables the Daleks to send such a Roboman on a mission without constantly having to issue instructions to it. Instead, they merely await its daily transmissions and adjust their plans as necessary.

A further enhancement of this new and frightening technology is the possibility for such internally implanted positronic discs being linked either directly to an individual Dalek's mind, or to the Dalek command net.

For the Daleks, the advantage of these new, enhanced Robomen over the 'humanoid' or Dalek 'replicant' is clear. Robomen are still human beings. They are flesh and blood, like you or me. Sophisticated security scanners can detect even the most elaborate androids, but Robomen read as real human beings. Only the most thorough and prolonged exposure to top-of-the-range security scan rays can detect the implanted positronic disc, and even now there is evidence that the energy field generated by the discs is being adjusted by the Daleks to imitate more closely the electrical activity of a normal human brain.

ETERNAL VIGILANCE

Therefore, the only sure route to the discovery of this new, deadlier breed of Roboman is *vigilance*. Never assume that the person you are talking to is untainted by the evil of the Daleks. Always be on your guard. Have they just asked you an unusual question? Are they trying to get you to reveal classified material?

Never confront them. Always take immediate, covert action to bring them before one of the more advanced security scans.

DALEK ALLIES – OGRONS

'Given a typewriter, an infinite number of monkeys might eventually write the compete works of Shakespeare. An infinite number of Ogrons will do nothing more than eat the typewriter.'

Primitive and ape-like, with mental abilities little higher than those of Earth's early cavemen, the Ogrons' vast strength and gullibility has meant that they are perfect for use by higher races as bodyguards and disposable foot soldiers.

The Daleks started using Ogron shock troops shortly after their Invasion of Earth in 2157, presumably because their natural stupidity made them easier to control than humans, and without the need for time-consuming robotization processes. This said, their Ogrons had to be equipped with suitably simplified technology – communicators with no more than one button, guns that required no magazine, and transport that they could keep upright.

The Ogrons originate from a desolate planet on the very edge of the Galaxy, but their culture is too primitive for them to have named it. For reporting purposes a committee has been assigned to arrive at a suitable designation for the planet of the Ogrons. Their recommendation is THE OGRON PLANET.

Although familiar with space travel and sophisticated weaponry, the Ogrons prefer to live in crude cave dwellings, their lifestyle similar to nomadic tribes found on the African subcontinent. Their society is feudal, with males often competing for supremacy in long and bloody battles. In the past these were fought with clubs, often lasting days, but with more and more space-faring races supplying them with sophisticated energy-weapons, these fights now last seconds.

The tricycle is the Ogrons' favourite mode of transport.

The most in-depth study of their race was carried out by the rogue scientist Dr Linus Leofrix, a maverick engaged in intelligence-enhancing experiments. At about the same time as Leofrix mysteriously vanished, reports started to come in from deep space operatives of an Ogron with above average intelligence, named Gnork. Investigations are proceeding into the possibility that these two events are connected in some way.

Although Ogrons are the principal foot soldiers of the Daleks they can be easily bribed and used against them. Operatives are therefore reminded to keep bananas in their survival kit if they are venturing into Ogron-controlled space.

Capture of Ogron prisoners is not recommended as they inevitably know nothing, take a lot of looking after, and smell horrible.

Notes to remember if intending to use Ogrons on operations:

1 **Do not** leave them instructions that can be misinterpreted.

2 **Do not** leave them instructions that need to be read.

3 **Do not** leave them instructions that can be eaten.

4 **Do not** leave them instructions.

5 **Do not** leave them (supervision recommended at all times).

DALEK SIGHTINGS THROUGH HISTORY

Although it is only recently that mankind at large has become aware of the Dalek threat, investigations by a team of dedicated archaeologists and historians have revealed that the Daleks have been on Earth many times throughout the centuries, no doubt on reconnaissance missions for their eventual invasion.

PALAEOLITHIC

Discovered in a cave at Worth Maltravers, Dorset.
POSSIBLE DALEK CONCLUSION: The humans' greatest weapon is the flint-tipped spear.

ANCIENT EGYPT

Discovered in the Great Pyramid. An interesting additional discovery was that of an anachronistic monk's habit nearby. Possibly, the Daleks, knowing the pyramids to be burial structures, brought with them a Dalek duplicate of a religious figure, but misjudged the period.

POSSIBLE DALEK CONCLUSION: Human beings will willingly drink poison in order to accompany their ruler to the afterlife.

■ ROMAN TIMES

Discovered when excavating one of the watchtowers on Hadrian's Wall. Other evidence suggests the Roman garrison repelled an attack by a single Dalek. Chronicles relate that the area was later obliterated by 'lightning from the stars'.

POSSIBLE DALEK CONCLUSION: Weight of numbers can be enough to drive off a single Dalek, even with primitive weaponry like spears and swords. Best to eliminate the whole area.

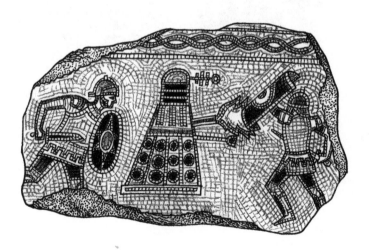

1066

POSSIBLE DALEK CONCLUSION: Humans never see what's right in front of them.

▮ WWII

Shell-shocked survivors report Dalek being destroyed
in the Blitz. Soldiers helping civilians to get to air-raid
shelters managed to bring down a wall on top of it.
POSSIBLE DALEK CONCLUSION: Keep away from
inefficient bricks-and-mortar building.

DALEK SURVEILLANCE

It is sometimes assumed that the Daleks have always possessed the potential to be masters of time and space. This is of course inaccurate. The Daleks have developed and evolved just as any other race has – except at several hundred times the speed of most other races, humans included. Nowhere is this more noticeable than in the realm of Dalek surveillance.

Early Daleks, aware that they needed to be wary of attackers visiting Skaro, created a primitive early-warning device known as the Perceptor. Working in a similar fashion to radar, the Perceptor beeped regularly and plaintively as it scanned the gates to the Dalek City. The closer someone – or something – got, the faster it beeped.

But initial Dalek enthusiasm soon waned. Operating in isolation, there was no way of telling whether the approaching life-form was a semi-petrified animal, a wandering Thal, or another Dalek. While Dalek death squads despatched to investigate the Perceptor's suspect beeps did so in energetic fashion for the first several hundred call-outs, inevitably such inefficiency was brought into question. Dalek operators in the control room, too, complained that the Perceptor's incessant beeping had a detrimental effect on their work ethic.

A Dalek death squad questioning an intruder.

After much discussion, scanners were subsequently installed at key strategic points around the city so that the Daleks could monitor these areas and observe when the Perceptor started pinging. This was something of a technological capitulation for the Dalek council.

Tentatively the Daleks introduced cheap monochrome technology, so as to avoid even drawing attention to the 'clear ruby' embarrassment among the Dalek masses. But when the definition proved unsatisfactory – for example, very small enemies, such as metallurgic mosquitoes from the Forbidden Islands, breaching the city were quite undetectable – full colour monitors were introduced. This breakthrough in surveillance technology was mirrored in the development of a sliding volume control to reduce the Perceptor's pings.

Discovering the colour monitor led to a breathtaking renaissance of invention in this long-suppressed branch of Dalek research. Bigger and better scanners were designed and built almost daily. Never again was a small butterfly passing the city gates the target of 20 shock Dalek troopers. And with internal security assured, the Daleks turned their artificial eyes out into space. Within three years of grudgingly installing their first internal television system, the Daleks created possibly the most advanced surveillance device in the galaxy – the Rangerscope.

Operated from the main Dalek City control room, it was a spying device with colossal range. Early models could merely locate activity on nearby satellites and planets, but improvements were made with horrifying speed. Within months the Rangerscope could detect activity in neighbouring solar systems, as well as visualize precise areas on other planets. The range increased as rapidly as the Daleks' war ambitions. Soon, all organic life throughout both spiral arms of the galaxy could be monitored and recorded at work and play. The shrill trills of the redundant Perceptor were finally silenced forever when its long-suffering operator was permitted to exterminate it.

Once it was discovered that worlds such as Mira, Refusis and Spiridon harboured invisible beings, it was decided that a mere visual surveillance device was not enough. So, in conjunction with the Rangerscope, a new device inimical to human freedom was developed – the Vibroscope. This chilling device detects all life-forms through their vibrations – even the vibrations in the fabric of space caused by spaceships in transit. Thus, any information – be it the louche activities of an invisible Visian, or the flight path of an Earth vessel

After one too many 'pings' the Perceptor was finally silenced forever.

ferrying grain to starving frontier worlds – can be assimilated and employed to aid the Daleks in their endless war against the universe. All that saves the universe from Dalek dominance is the massive amount of time such cosmic note-taking demands – particularly since the Daleks operate on a four-dimensional plane. Ever on the lookout for some inherent weakness in an enemy's history that they may exploit, they have been, are, and always shall be chronicling an extremely lengthy history of time – a chilling new twist on the Daleks' ancient reputation of academic excellence in the humanities (see: *Time-Space Visualizer.*)

Remember, at all times you may be being watched.

The Dalek Rangerscope can penetrate all visual barriers – spying through cloud cover, brick walls, clothing and even the skin to analyse activity in a subject's body at a molecular level.

WHAT TO DO: Act as innocently as possible at all times, even when engaged in vital anti-Dalek covert work, so as not to arouse attention. It is mandatory for active agents to surround themselves by objects that 'ping' – Daleks have developed an aversion to this noise and will usually spy elsewhere on reflex.

▉ WATCH YOUR MOVES

The Daleks, like any life-form monitoring the activities of a race perceived to be of lesser worth, soon tire of boring subjects. Consider the human watching ants in a formicarium. If the ants do nothing, the human tires and wanders off, to return later.

WHAT TO DO: Punctuate urgent covert activities with long periods of inactivity. No matter how demoralizing and repugnant it may seem to put your feet up, rest and do nothing at all for hours at a stretch in the middle of a potentially fatal act of espionage, remember you are doing it for the greater good of Earth. He who hesitates is indeed lost – to Dalek scrutiny.

DALEK EQUIPMENT

TRANSOLAR DISCS

The Dalek transolar disc (as depicted here) has been described as 'universally feared'. At first, this may seem odd, especially since the Daleks have other craft in their armoury such as the Dalek Cleaver (a drill-nosed spacecraft able to hurl itself at mountain-sized objects and bore through without any loss of speed), the Megallanic Cloud Cruiser and the Skaro Screamer (capable of turning the atmosphere on any planet into liquid oxygen for its own propulsion and rearming purposes).

The transolar disc is formidable in space battle situations.

Military psychologists, however, have, after exhaustive case studies and interviews, discovered that the simple reason why the transolar disc is so universally feared is that it is the only Dalek craft that leaves its Dalek pilot fully on display.

Imagine the scenario:

You are on a planet and you know the Daleks are going to attack. After bombardment from Dalek saucers in orbit, you know all your planetary defences have been knocked out. What now?

An eerie silence falls upon the devastated landscape you once thought of as your beautiful home planet. As the metallic dust of destruction clears, there is a faint buzzing sound on the choking breeze. The sound grows and grows until it is almost an unbearable scream. Then, suddenly, through the clouds emerge tens of thousands of transolar discs, all of them reflecting harsh silver light as the dull sun glints off the polished armour of countless Dalek battle drones. And there they all are, not hidden inside saucers, but sitting atop these discs of destruction, twitching their guns in anticipation, swivelling their domed head sections excitedly, their lights flashing... you can hear them barking commands to each other. You are face to face with almost certain death, and as the exterminations begin

with the first swoop of the first squadron, you can
see the burning light of what seems like each and
every Dalek eye stalk in the universe.

In effect, the transolar disc allows the Daleks to create
their own version of the blitzkrieg. Violent, sudden,
brutal and somehow, almost personal.

There are, of course, a number of disc types. Some
have been spotted with weaponry attachments to the
main body of the disc. These weapons are operated by
the Dalek manipulating controls on the disc railings.
Indeed, the special connection between the Dalek's
sucker attachment and the transolar disc affords an
almost symbiotic relationship between Dalek and disc.
This high level of sensitivity in the Dalek's control of
the disc's movements make it formidable in space battle
situations and unshakeable in its pursuit of victims
running for cover on the ground. The directional
thrusters of the disc make it more manoeuvrable than a
Dalek in independent hover mode.

Surprisingly, it is still unclear how a Dalek prefers to
exit from a transolar disc, since there have been so few
survivors left to give detailed accounts, but our experts
lean towards the theory that Daleks hover in and out
of their discs.

It is worth noting that the transolar disc is often
referred to as a *hoverbout* when it is engaged in routine

The Dalek Cleaver.

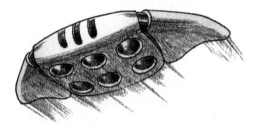

The Megallanic Cloud Cruiser.

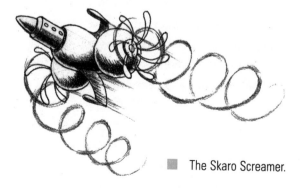

The Skaro Screamer.

patrol operations within a planet's atmosphere.
However, since the discs are usually fitted with high-energy interplanetary drive systems, they should more accurately be identified as transolar discs, for the purposes of sighting reports.

THE TIME-SPACE VISUALIZER – A LESSON IN TIME TRAVEL

We have known for some time that the Daleks have fully functional time-travel technology that aids them in their chronicling of the web of time. However, while they chronicle, they do not interfere with history. If they fail once, they never try to go back in time to try again. This is because Daleks have been involved in temporal paradoxes before, and find them ultimately irritating, counter-productive to their war effort, and extremely confusing to chronicle. For instance, one very promising time-line where the Daleks successfully invaded Earth in the 22nd century was entirely reversed by time-active rebels travelling back to the 20th century. While most Daleks accepted this annoying paradox stoically, a total of three despairing Daleks went back to the 20th century to ensure their future survived. Predictably, as the Dalek scholars could have told them, they failed.

But not only is the monitoring of every event in the

universe a time-consuming activity: it is also quite a dull one. Often, criminal Daleks are sentenced to serve time in a special prison facility where they are ordered to add to the chronicles for centuries at a time as a form of community service.

During routine surveillance of a known enemy – a traveller in space and time known as the Doctor – the criminal Daleks ignored a paradox alert (no Daleks are permitted to cause paradoxes by witnessing their own timelines). They observed the Doctor using a nonsensical device that worked essentially like a 'time television'. He was tuning in to events in the human past. Scanning ahead, they observed the Doctor using the device to observe a squad of Daleks in pursuit of his time machine.

The Daleks were intrigued. Such a device as the Time-Space Visualizer (as they called it) was scientifically impossible. It could only work if every event in history gave off a visual mass whose light neutrons could be converted into electrical impulses – which it doesn't. Such activities could only be observed by physically angling a Dalek Rangerscope at desired locations in real-time. The Time-Space Visualizer was clearly some kind of hoax.

At this point – just before the Rangerscope's paradox failsafes cut in – a cell of bored criminal Daleks recognized the Daleks in the transmission as themselves. Clearly, to be sure they would be free to pursue the Doctor through all Eternity, these Daleks would have to construct the Time-Space Visualizer themselves. Then the Doctor would be able to pick up the observed transmission of them leaving to chase him. The ringleader declared they would humiliate their greatest enemy, and ensure their own escape. Paradoxically, by playing the hoax themselves, they would write their freedom into recorded history.

It was a task approached with typical Dalek efficiency. The criminals constructed the Time-Space Visualizer out of equipment in the prison kitchens. It was inevitably unwieldy, not only in sheer size but in operation. On the machine's control panel they assembled a long vertical list of all the planets in the universe. Then, in a pocket dimension fitted into a filing drawer beneath a (black-and-white) monitor screen they prepared small maps of each square mile of each planet in the cosmos – just in case their quarry suspected a bluff.

The Daleks had already observed which scenes the Doctor and his friends would view on the scanner. So they took enslaved humans (also held in the prison facility) and recorded these same scenes on the Rangerscope. They knew in advance from their observations that the Doctor and his friends would never suspect they were watching a cheap and cheerful

performance rather than real history. These scenes were
then dubbed down on to a video cassette, to convince
their foe that the machine really worked. That done,
the Dalek criminals smuggled themselves out of the
archival prisons (pretending to pursue an unconvincing
robot double of the Doctor adapted from a faulty
food-mixer through the Dalek city) and into a time
machine.

Far from being incensed, the Dalek authorities were
amused, and actively encouraged the Dalek criminals'
activities. These dissidents were a group whose
intelligence and motor skills were considered remedial
at best. The Dalek Supreme offered them full pardons
if they could exterminate the Doctor. For the
amusement of all legitimate Dalek chroniclers, the
activities of the group of criminals in their ship were
broadcast in full colour around the planet. What all the
other Daleks knew was that had these dissident Daleks
seen the end of their quest for glory before the
Rangerscope's paradox fail-safes cut in, they would
probably have stayed at home.

The criminals' first mistake occurred while dumping
the Time-Space Visualizer in a space museum on
Xeros. The Dalek assigned to the task was
unfortunately killed by a vengeful curator attempting
to secure the admission charge, and became one of the
exhibits. After a frenetic chase through time and space

they ultimately failed miserably in all their attempts to execute a single frail old man, and were finally destroyed by some robotic house-cleaners on the jungle planet Mechanus.

The paradox was played out, the broadcasts rammed home the dangers and tedium of such paradoxes, the criminals were purged from the timelines, and the Daleks, council and chroniclers alike, returned to the real business of observing, assessing and plotting their masterplans.

ANTI-GRAVITATIONAL DISCS

Anti-gravity is a scientific breakthrough that the Daleks have used in many of their technologies – transolar discs, space saucers, and so on. The anti-gravitational disc is perhaps the purest application of this technology, and it raises a question mark over another application that the Daleks initially missed. The anti-gravitational disc, or AGD, is essentially a raised, circular platform about 30 cm thick. The platform is slightly larger than the base of a Dalek. A shallow ramp leads up to it, allowing a Dalek to take up position on the disc.

Once the Dalek is in position, energy levels build until the disc has enough power to operate its anti-gravitational field. The AGD, with the Dalek on it, rises into the air. Some models of AGD allow the operator Dalek a degree of directional control, not unlike that of a transolar disc. However, the AGD is rather less sophisticated, and such manoeuvres are best kept to a minimum. Not least as, unlike a transolar disc, the anti-gravitational disc has no guard rails round the edge to prevent the Dalek from sliding off if it gets too adventurous in its aerobatics.

Until recently, we believed we had cause for optimism, in that we thought that we had spotted a

It is distressing to note that we can no longer be sure of escaping a Dalek by merely running upstairs.

potential application of the technology which the Daleks themselves had missed. However, video data recently acquired suggests that the Daleks have finally realized the potential of their anti-gravitational technology. They have at last spotted that the size and shape of an anti-gravitational disc are roughly the same as the size and shape of the base of a Dalek, and have built the technology into their casings.

Among the other discouraging implications of the Daleks' belated discovery, not least is the fact that we can no longer be sure of escaping from a Dalek simply by running upstairs.

THE DALEKS – ARE THEY ALL BAD?

▷ On interception of a Thal distress signal, a neighbouring race sent out a negotiation team to settle a peace between the warring factions. Their initial report appears below:

When they first came on the scene, we saw the Daleks only in black and white.

Even the most enlightened observers thought of the Daleks in terms of Absolute Evil. They saw a race that killed and conquered, that suppressed without mercy and exterminated everyone in sight. And they decided that this was a *bad thing*. They looked no further. They did not ask themselves: where is the culture of the Daleks that we should seek out and appreciate?

And this is an important consideration. All through history we have made the mistake of only seeing the bad in other races. It took centuries for the so-called 'civilized world' to appreciate the art and culture of other peoples, to look more than skin-deep. Have we learnt nothing?

When we see the Daleks exterminate hundreds of people, we should not simply condemn. We must ask ourselves: 'Where is the Art in this? What does it tell us about this race?'

Do they, for example, simply fire a blanket ray that

turns everything negative? Or is there a subtle 'halo' effect? Perhaps the weaponry used illuminates for a brief moment the skeleton within the victim – a tantalizing glimpse of the inner self, a subtle plea from the Dalek for us to look further than external appearances.

For the Dalek creatures are themselves protected by their casings. They are, almost by definition, more than skin deep. Sadly, we may never perceive them as warm and cuddly, but they are, in very real terms, soft centred.

Think of the way the Dalek casing is constructed. The half-globes in the lower area may be a deliberate attempt to soften the shape and make it less intimidating. Consider the sucker arm – a device surely designed to make explicit the Daleks' desire to draw out sympathy, to suck our love from us.

Because, after all, deep down, the Daleks just want to be loved. Why else would they behave as they do? Like errant teenagers, their violence and aggression is a plea for help – for understanding and individuality in their mechanized society. How can they ever learn, ever come to terms with their true feelings and emotions if we do not help them?

Don't perpetuate the vicious circle of aggression and misunderstanding. Don't just run away next time a Dalek approaches you. Talk to it, get to understand it, appreciate it. Remember the Dalek's perspective is just as valid as your own. All right, so you may not actually want to be exterminated, but try to appreciate – for once – the Dalek's point of view.

If you do, then maybe you can come to some arrangement, start the process of give and take.

So next time the Daleks invade your planet, burn down your cities and ruthlessly exterminate everyone in sight – spare a thought for *them*. Ask yourself: they may have conquered half the galaxy and built a huge empire, they may have subjugated all the races of the Third Region and decimated Calister-Minor, but – when it comes down to it – are the Daleks really happy?

▷ The return of the negotiators is still awaited.

SECTION
3

FREQUENTLY ASKED QUESTIONS

Q How do Daleks reproduce?

A Reproduction for the Daleks is more of a laboratory process than a biological one. Reports vary, and not surprisingly, it is hardly an area where agents are keen to focus their attentions. But it seems that embryo Daleks are cultured in bio-tanks. When they reach maturity they are transplanted from the nutrient-rich

fluid in which they are stored into Dalek casings. Once inside the casing they are hooked up to the nutrient and control systems. Positronic linkages are then activated which interface with other Dalek technology and equipment.

Q How are Dalek casings made?

A The Dalek casings are produced in huge factories on Skaro. The Daleks also have factory facilities built into some models of their spacecraft. The factories are fully automated, components being laid out for robotic inspection, and then fitted together on a conveyor belt. At the end of the process, Dalek creatures are lowered into the completed casings, the dome section is fixed in place, and the completed Dalek rolls off the end of the production line.

Q Do the Daleks have their own language?

A The Daleks have sophisticated technology that instantly translates their speech into all the languages of life-forms within hearing, to ensure that each life-form hears the Dalek in its own language. This technology is so advanced that it even works on recorded material.

So, while there have been attempts to compile 'Dalek dictionaries', it is actually impossible to tell what language the Daleks really speak. In fact, in many ways it is an invalid question. One theory is that the Daleks communicate with each other by direct telepathic projection. If this is true then they cannot rely on simply hearing which direction speech is coming from to tell which Dalek is talking – which may explain why they flash their lights: it is to indicate when a Dalek is speaking.

Q What does a Dalek creature look like?

A Sightings of the actual creatures have been few and far between, and reports on their appearance differ widely. One of the more reliable sources describes them as 'small, green, blob-like octopods with claws', but this objective tone is rare, and most descriptions are along the more emotive lines of 'living, bubbling lumps of hate', as one observer put it.

The entrance to Dalek City.

Q Where do the Daleks live?

A They live in the underground Dalek City on Skaro, their home planet. Notable features of the city include the Emperor's throne room, the War Museum, and the Dome of Science and Culture, where great Dalek advances are celebrated.

Q Can Daleks see the colour red?

A This issue has caused confusion in the past, but the fact that Supreme Controller Daleks are themselves red suggests that the colour is perfectly visible to them. There is evidence that very early-model Daleks could only see in black and white, which might explain how the misunderstanding arose.

Q What do Daleks do for entertainment?

A They occasionally enjoy watching re-runs of great Dalek victories, but their true passion is for reconnaissance – a Dalek will go to any lengths to gather new information, and they often put themselves at great risk to do so.

Q Are the Daleks totally indestructible, or do they have any weak areas?

A Over the millennia the Daleks have constantly developed and refined themselves into one of the most terrifying and extreme killing machines known to man. Their casings are heavily armoured, they are equipped with a variety of deadly weapons, and they have absolutely no capacity for pity or remorse. With these facts in mind the prognosis isn't good. However, it is within this almost indestructible level of strength that we find the Daleks' primary, and possibly only, weakness – overconfidence. The Daleks are so used to considering themselves invincible that they have no capacity to adapt to failure. The notions of tactical retreat or strategic withdrawal are alien to them, and for this reason, failure, when it occurs, is always spectacular.

Q Do the Daleks have any natural enemies?

A The Daleks regard every other life form as hostile, with very few exceptions – there are life forms they 'use' like the Ogrons, the Slyther and the Varga Plant. According to our information, the first enemy of the Daleks was the Thals. Other races that have successfully opposed the Daleks are few and far between, though the Movellans are worthy of mention.

The Movellans seem to be a race of humanoids, though there are rumours that they may in fact be robots. They developed a virus that attacked the Dalek creatures within their casings and wrought havoc on the Dalek Empire. The Daleks were forced to retreat and regroup until they had found an antidote for the virus.

Q Can Daleks swim?

A There is currently no *absolute* data on this subject, though there are rumoured to be plans in existence for a Dalek Submarine and we are aware of underwater Special Weapons Daleks.

Since Daleks are equipped to travel through space without extra protection, they can probably operate underwater as well. There are unconfirmed reports of Daleks being sighted emerging from the Thames.

Q Can Daleks climb stairs?

A There is still a perception that Daleks cannot climb stairs. However, it has been known since the early 1960s that Dalek anti-gravitational technology in fact allows them to levitate their casings, and move smoothly up a flight of steps. This same technology allows them to navigate over rough terrain.

Q Do Daleks sleep?

A Daleks are able to utilize
different sections of their
brain at different times, so
while some parts are
resting, the remainder will
carry on processing
information and operating
the Dalek machine. A
Dalek cannot be caught
unawares.

Q Who are the Thals?

A The Thals are a race of humanoid people who inhabit
Skaro – the Dalek planet. Before the war that
decimated Skaro, the Thals were a race of warriors and
the Daleks' ancestors, the Kaleds, were teachers and
philosophers.

After the war the Thals that survived managed to
cultivate small plots of land, becoming farmers.

After the great war, most of the Thals died and the
survivors mutated. But, unlike the Daleks', the Thals'
mutation came full circle then refined itself over
hundreds of years into the tall, slim, blond human
beings that the Thals have become.

Now the Thals have evolved into a race of pacifists –

absolutely morally opposed to conflict, although there are reports that they organise resistance against the Daleks both on Skaro and on other planets.

Q What is a Slyther?

A The Daleks occasionally use these revolting creatures as 'guard dogs' while patrolling alien planets. It is not known where the Slyther first originated from, but there are whole hordes of them now living on Skaro. The Slyther survives by ingesting organic life-forms – the Dalek casings are indigestible to it, so Daleks are safe.

Q What is a Varga Plant?

A Little is known of the Varga Plant, though it is mentioned in the *Dalek Chronicles*. In appearance it resembles a furry cactus, approximately the size of a man – although photographic evidence indicates that some plants may grow to be as tall as a block of flats.

Our sources suggest that the Varga Plant is used by the Daleks as a defence mechanism. Its thorns are poisonous and inject a spore-venom that, over time, transform the life form into a Varga Plant. This interesting method of reproduction may help to explain reports of Varga plants moving, and even hunting down further victims.

There are fierce debates between horticulturists and naturalists as to whether the Varga should be counted as a animal or vegetable. But researchers tend not to return from field trips.

(Q) If the Daleks do invade – what will happen?

(A) It is a long held belief that a meteorite storm will be the first indication of a Dalek attack. Intelligence data suggests that the Daleks will divert asteroids from the vicinity of Saturn, and set them on a collision course for Earth. Their intention is to stretch the emergency and defence forces of our planet to breaking point.

It is then that the Daleks will land in force.

(Q) What is our main defence?

(A) The force charged with defending Earth from alien incursion and attack in UNIT – the United Nations Intelligence Taskforce. This multinational organisation, under the auspices of the UN, is controlled from Geneva. The British section is staffed by military personnel seconded from the regular armed services.

Q Are the Daleks more likely to attack now than in the past? And if so, why?

A It is only in the last 50 years that Man has ventured into space. From the first communications satellites and Yuri Gagarin's historic space flight, we have sent probes further and further out into the solar system – and beyond. Up until then, Earth was insignificant and as far as other space-going races were aware uninhabited by intelligent life. But now we are drawing attention to ourselves. Every space mission, every launch of the Shuttle, every satellite and probe serves to indicate that there is life on Earth – life that may have resources and talents that could be useful to the Daleks; life that may one day stray further from its home planet and threaten the Dalek Empire...

GLOSSARY

ANTI-GRAVITATIONAL DISC A Dalek device that negates gravity so that a Dalek can hover above the ground or even ascend into the air.

BRYANT ANDERSON REPORT Bryant Anderson was a scientist commissioned to discover fatal weaknesses in the Daleks by studying their essential nature. Fragments of his report, recovered from a covert mission to the planet Ollendorf 2, were decoded by Terry Nation, and give an account of how the Daleks might have been created.

DALEK An intelligent and aggressive alien life-form from the planet Skaro. The Dalek creatures live inside protective, armoured casings. The main objective of the Daleks is to exterminate all other life-forms and become the dominant species of the universe.

DALEK CREATURE The creature that actually lives inside the Dalek casing. Descriptions are rare, but the general agreement is that the creature is horribly grotesque – a 'living, bubbling lump of hate' according to one account.

DALEKENIUM The metal from which the bulk of the Dalek casing is made. It is immensely tough and durable, and Dalek spacecraft and other technologies are also made from it. In unrefined, volatile form, Dalekenium is a powerful explosive that can rupture a Dalek casing or – in sufficient quantity – destroy a large building in what is essentially a 'clean' nuclear blast.

DALEK SUPREME There is some debate as to whether all Daleks on the Council are 'Supreme Daleks' or 'Supreme Controllers' etc., or whether the 'Dalek Supreme' is a rank in its own right within the Council, second only to the Emperor.

DALS One version of Dalek history gives the name of the race that evolved into the Daleks as 'Dals' (see also *Kaleds*).

DAVROS Crippled Kaled scientist. He experimented to determine the ultimate form of the Kaled race, as mutated by the chemical and biological weapons of the war with the Thals. Davros introduced genetic alterations into the mutation to create the Dalek as we know it – a creature without feeling or pity, utterly ruthless and determined to survive at the expense of all other life-forms.

■ **DOCTOR, THE** A mythic figure reputed to be the Daleks' ultimate enemy. He is also rumoured to be Scientific Advisor to UNIT. Possibly a Time Lord.

■ **DRENZ** Pacifist leader of the Dals, according to one version of Dalek history.

■ **EMPEROR DALEK** The leader of the Dalek race and its commander in chief.

■ **'EXTERMINATE!'** Dalek battle cry. Daleks have also been heard to use other words and phrases including (but not limited to): 'Seek, locate, exterminate', 'Daleks conquer and destroy', 'Advance and attack, attack and destroy, destroy and rejoice.'

■ **HOVERBOUT** see *Transolar Disc*

■ **KALEDS** The most widely accepted version of Dalek history gives the name of the race that evolved into the Daleks as 'Kaleds' (see also *Dals*).

■ **LAKE OF MUTATIONS** A large body of water behind the Dalek City of Skaro. The lake is so named because it is home to monstrous mutated creatures that resulted from the chemical and radioactive fallout of the Thal–Kaled war.

LUMINOSITY DISCHARGERS Things that look like light bulbs on the top of a Dalek's head. They illuminate when the Dalek speaks.

NATION, TERRY Television writer who discovered and translated the *Dalek Chronicles* and documented Dalek history for BBC Television.

OGRONS Monstrous ape-like creatures used by the Daleks as security agents. They work like guard dogs, but are somewhat less intelligent.

PERCEPTOR Primitive Dalek early-warning device that bleeped when an enemy approached. Superseded by the Rangerscope (qv).

PETRIFIED JUNGLE A forest close to the Dalek City on Skaro. The intense heat of the neutron bomb that devastated the planet turned the trees to stone and the soil to sand and ash.

POWER SLATS Vertical slats round a Dalek's middle section that absorb sunlight and ambient radiation to be converted into motive power for the Dalek.

RANGERSCOPE A Dalek visual surveillance device with tremendous range.

ROBOMAN A human who has been 'robotized' by the Daleks to turn him (or her) into a mindless automaton obedient to the Daleks' will. Robomen eventually 'burn out' and kill themselves.

SENSE GLOBES The hemispherical globes on the lower part of a Dalek's casing replace the external sense organs of the Dalek that are not already catered for (such as the sense of smell).

SKARO Home planet of the Daleks. Also home to the surviving Thals.

SLYTHER An unpleasant, slimy creature that lives on Skaro. Used as a guard by the Daleks because of its diet of organic flesh.

SPECIAL WEAPONS DALEK A type of Dalek bred entirely for destruction – a 'blunt' weapon with little intelligence or reasoning abilities other than those necessary for total war.

SUCKER CUP The usual attachment on the Dalek's main 'arm' although other devices and tools can be fitted (for example, flame thrower, cutting tool or portable Perceptor).

SUPREME COUNCIL The Dalek ruling body, presided over by the Emperor.

SUPREME DALEK see *Dalek Supreme*

THALS Humanoid natives of the planet Skaro and traditional enemies of the Daleks.

TIME LORDS A race of extremely powerful alien beings who can travel in and manipulate time itself. The Doctor (qv) may be a Time Lord.

TIME/SPACE VISUALIZER A device that uses ambient light energy and proton-preservation to show images of the past.

TRANSOLAR DISC Also known colloquially as a 'Hoverbout', the Transolar Disc is a one-Dalek aircraft of incredible speed and manoeuvrability.

UNIT United Nations Intelligence Taskforce – the military body charged by the UN with investigating and negating all alien threats to Earth. The British branch of UNIT is accountable only to UNIT HQ in Geneva, though it is monitored by the Ministry of Defence.

VARGA PLANT A large furry semi-mobile cactus with poisonous thorns indigenous to Skaro, though exported by the Daleks to other planets such as Kemble. Once stung by a Varga thorn, the victim mutates into a Varga plant.

VIBROSCOPE A Dalek device that detects life-forms through their vibrations – even the vibrations in the fabric of space caused by spaceships.

YARVELLING Chief scientist of the Dals, according to one version of Dalek history.

ZOLFIAN War minister of the Dals, according to one version of Dalek history.